EASIEST KEYBOARD COLLECTION

Today's Hit Songs

Published by
Wise Publications

Exclusive Distributors:
Music Sales Limited
14-15 Berners Street,
London W1T 3LJ, UK.
Music Sales Pty Limited
Units 3-4, 17 Willfox Street, Condell Park
NSW 2200, Australia.

Order No. AM1009371
ISBN: 978-1-78305-694-1
This book © Copyright 2014 Wise Publications.

Edited by Jenni Norey.
Music arranged by Vasco Hexel.
Music processed by Paul Ewers Music Design.

Printed in the EU.

Your Guarantee of Quality
As publishers, we strive to produce every book to the highest
commercial standards.
Particular care has been given to specifying acid-free, neutral-sized
paper made from pulps which have not been elemental chlorine
bleached. This pulp is from farmed sustainable forests and was
produced with special regard for the environment.
Throughout, the printing and binding have been planned to ensure
a sturdy, attractive publication which should give years of enjoyment.
If your copy fails to meet our high standards, please inform us and
we will gladly replace it.

www.musicsales.com

EASIEST KEYBOARD COLLECTION

Today's Hit Songs

WISE PUBLICATIONS
part of The Music Sales Group
London/New York/Paris/Sydney/Copenhagen/Berlin/Madrid/Hong Kong/Tokyo

Contents

ALL OF ME

Words & Music by John Legend & Tobias Gad

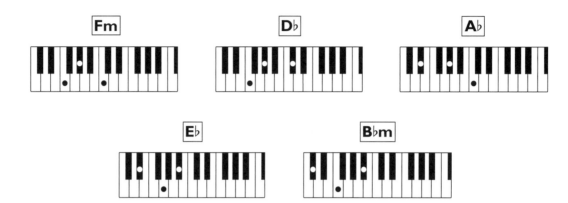

Voice: **Tenor Saxophone**

Rhythm: **Slow Rock**

Tempo: ♩ = 128

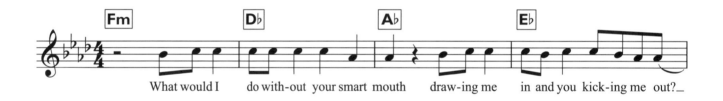

What would I do with-out your smart mouth draw-ing me in and you kick-ing me out?

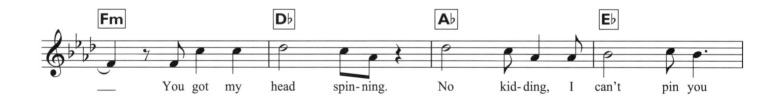

You got my head spin-ning. No kid-ding, I can't pin you

down. What's go-ing on in that beau-ti-ful mind? I'm on your ma-gi-cal mys-te-ry ride,

and I'm so diz-zy. Don't know what hit me. But I'll be al-

HAND ON HEART

Words & Music by Wayne Hector, Thomas Barnes, Peter Kelleher, Benjamin Kohn, Iain James & Oliver Murs

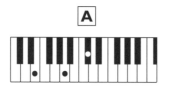
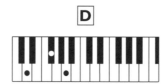

Voice: **Acoustic Guitar**

Rhythm: **Folk Rock**

Tempo: ♩ = 88

Come on,____ come on,____ I'm right,____ I'm wrong..

___ And when_ I'm wrong I say.___ We al - ways had___ the good,_ the bad_

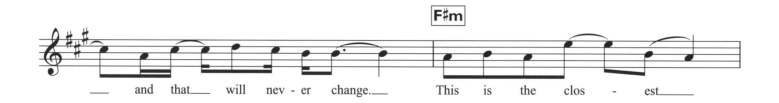

___ and that___ will nev - er change.___ This is the clos - est___

I've ev - er been.___ Oh, yeah.___

We give,_ we take._ We meet,_ we break___ and so___ the cy - cle goes.

We're do - ing well,_ we've been_ through hell_ and on - ly heav-en knows_

how far we get_ to._ Thank God I met_ you though._

_ And if you don't know... Just put your hand on my heart._

_ Put your hand on my heart._ And I don't have to say_

_ it._ And I don't have to fake_ it._ Just put your hand on my heart._

_ Just put your hand on my heart._

_ And you'd_ know._

9

HAPPY

Words & Music by Pharrell Williams

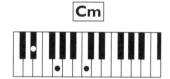
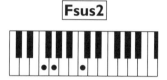

Voice: **Alto Saxophone**

Rhythm: **Beat Rock**

Tempo: ♩ = 156

It might seem cra - zy what I'm 'bout to say.____

Sun - shine,___ she's here,___ you can take a break.___

___ I'm a hot air bal - loon___

___ that could go to space____ with the air,___

___ like I don't care,___ ba - by, by the way._____ (Be - cause I'm

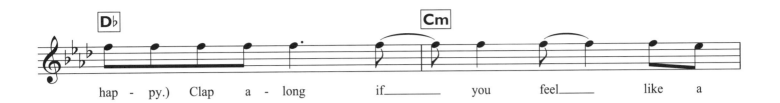

hap - py.) Clap a - long if_____ you feel_____ like a

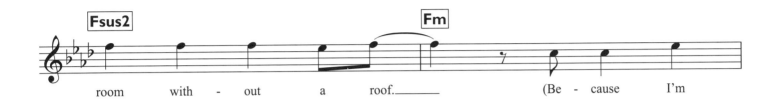

room with - out a roof._____ (Be - cause I'm

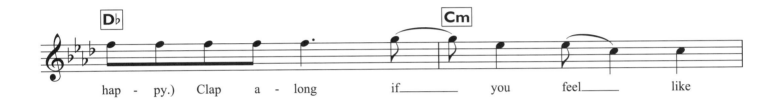

hap - py.) Clap a - long if_____ you feel_____ like

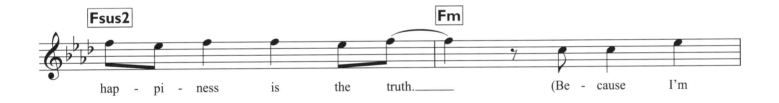

hap - pi - ness is the truth._____ (Be - cause I'm

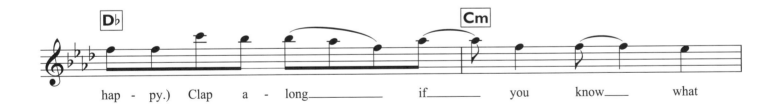

hap - py.) Clap a - long_____ if_____ you know_____ what

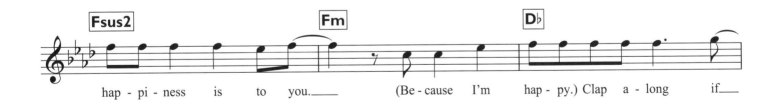

hap - pi - ness is to you._____ (Be - cause I'm hap - py.) Clap a - long if_____

____ you feel_____ like that's what you wan - na do._____

11

HEY BROTHER

Words & Music by Tim Bergling, Vincent Pontare, Ash Pournouri, Salem Al Fakir & Veronica Maggio

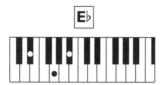
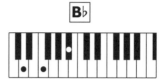
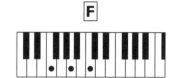

Voice: **Lead Synth**

Rhythm: **Dance Pop**

Tempo: ♩ = 132

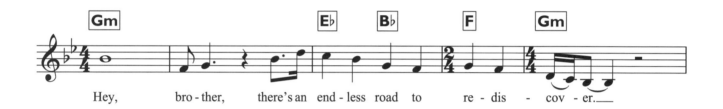

Hey, bro-ther, there's an end-less road to re-dis-cov-er.

Hey, sis-ter, know the wa-ter's sweet but blood is thick-er.

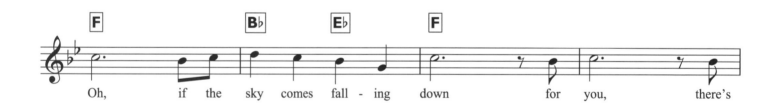

Oh, if the sky comes fall-ing down for you, there's

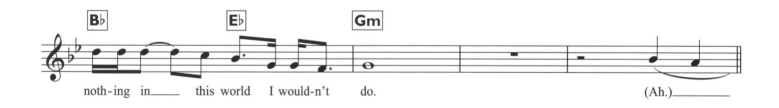

noth-ing in____ this world I would-n't do. (Ah.)_____

____ What if I'm far from__ home? Oh, bro-ther I__ will hear you call.__

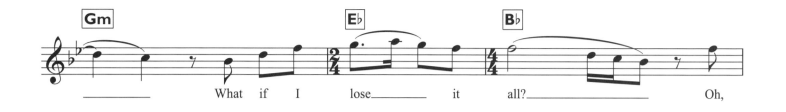

_____ What if I lose_____ it all?_____ Oh,

sis - ter I will help you out.__ Oh, if the sky comes fall - ing down for

you, there's noth-ing in__ this world I would-n't do.

13

HOW LONG WILL I LOVE YOU

Words & Music by Mike Scott

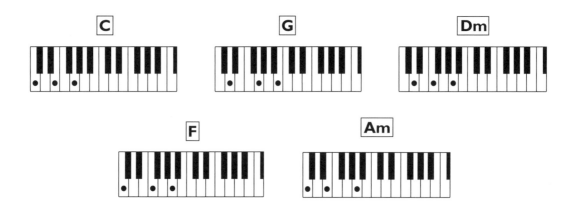

Voice: **Piano**

Rhythm: **Slow Rock**

Tempo: ♩ = 60

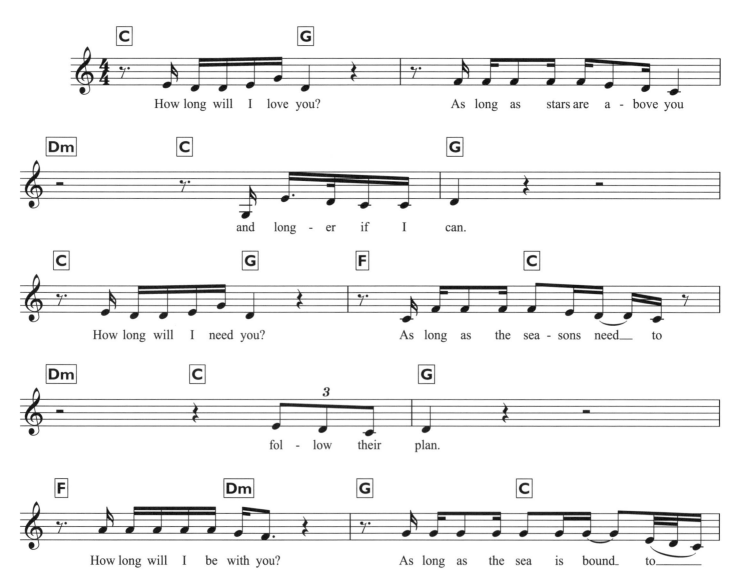

wash up - on the sand.

How long will I love__ you?__ As long as stars are a - bove you

and long - er if I may.__

Mm.__

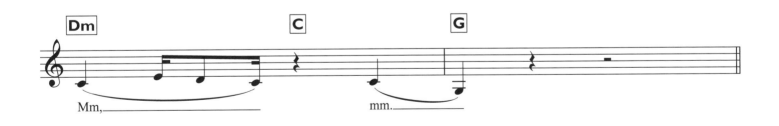

Mm,__ mm.__

How long will I love you? As long as stars are a - bove you.

15

INTO THE BLUE

Words & Music by Kelly Sheehan, Jacob Hindlin, Michael Gonzalez & Marco Lisboa

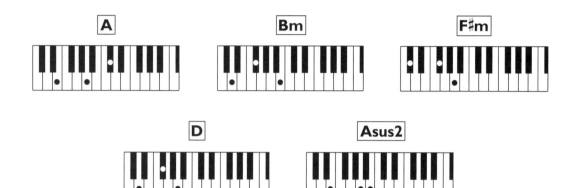

Voice: **Vibraphone**

Rhythm: **Dance Pop**

Tempo: ♩ = 116

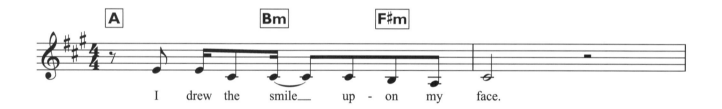

I drew the smile__ up - on my face.

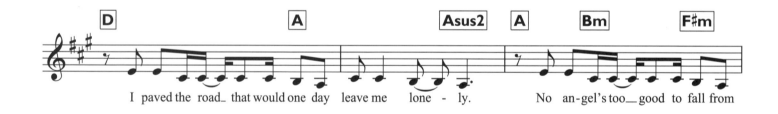

I paved the road__ that would one day leave me lone - ly. No an-gel's too__ good to fall from

grace. If she lets go__ of what-ev - er keeps her__ ho - ly.

I'm still__ here__ hold-ing on__ so tight to ev - 'ry - thing__ that I left__

___ be - hind.___ I don't_ care___ if the world___ is mine 'cause

this is___ all___ I know.___ When I got my back___ up a - gainst the wall___

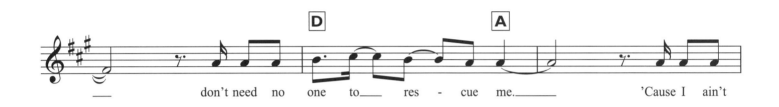

___ don't need no one to___ res - cue me.___ 'Cause I ain't

wait-ing up___ for no mi - ra - cle.___ Yeah, to - night I'm___ run - ning free.___

___ In - to the___ blue.___ In - to the___

blue___ with noth - ing to___ lose.___

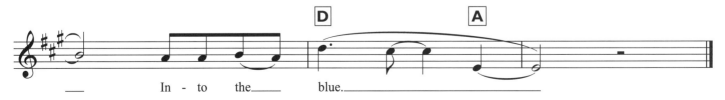

___ In - to the___ blue.___

17

IT'S MY PARTY

Words & Music by Claude Kelly, Jessica Cornish, John Lardieri & Colin Norman
© Copyright 2013 Warner Tamerlane Publishing Corporation/Studio Beast Music /Bat Radar Music/3M Holdings.
Notting Hill Music (UK) Limited/Sony/ATV Music Publishing/Warner/Chappell North America Limited/
Kobalt Music Publishing Limited/Copyright Control.
All Rights Reserved. International Copyright Secured.

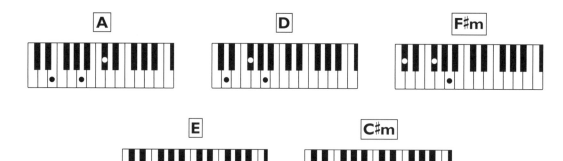

Voice: **Electric Guitar**

Rhythm: **Hard Rock**

Tempo: ♩ = 128

You're stuck in the play-ground___ and I'm a grown wom-an now.___ Con-

-sid-er-ing you hate me, you're stalk-ing like you made me. So why you

act-ing like___you're tough? By now I thought you'd had___ e-nough. Don't you get

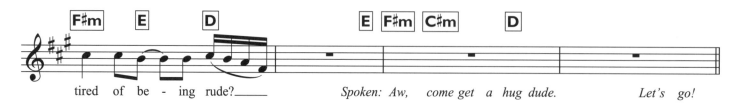

tired of be-ing rude?___ *Spoken: Aw,* come get a hug dude. *Let's go!*

It's my_ par - ty. I'll do, do what I want._ Do, do what I want._

_ So, while you sit and_ watch_ me I'll keep danc - ing a - lone._

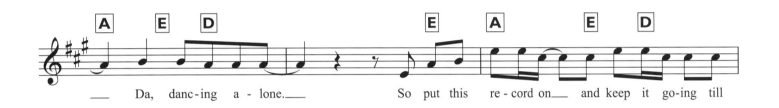

_ Da, danc - ing a - lone._ So put this re - cord on_ and keep it go-ing till

I say_ stop. If you were wond-'rin' if_ I give a damn,_ well, I do_ not._ 'Cause

it's my_ par - ty. I'll do, do what I want._ Do, do what I want._

_ Whoa._ Whoa._

Whoa._ Whoa._

KIDS AGAIN

Words & Music by Fraser Thorneycroft-Smith & Elliot Gleave

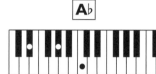

Voice: **Lead Synth**

Rhythm: **Techno**

Tempo: ♩ = 128

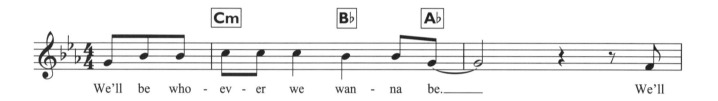

We'll be who - ev - er we wan - na be._____ We'll

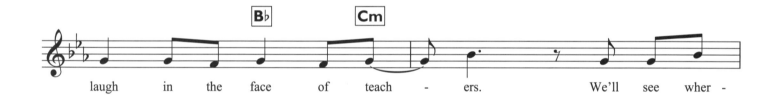

laugh in the face of teach - ers. We'll see wher -

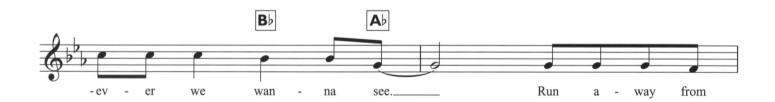

-ev - er we wan - na see._____ Run a - way from

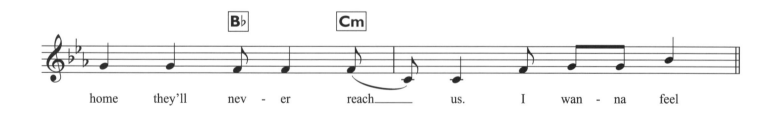

home they'll nev - er reach_____ us. I wan - na feel

oh, so young to - day._____ I don't wan - na

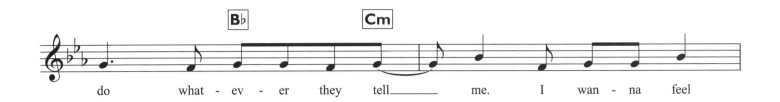

do what-ev-er they tell_____ me. I wan - na feel

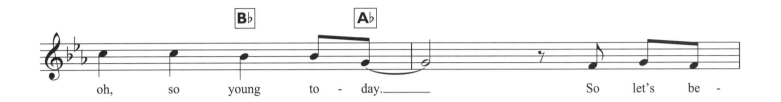

oh, so young to - day._____ So let's be -

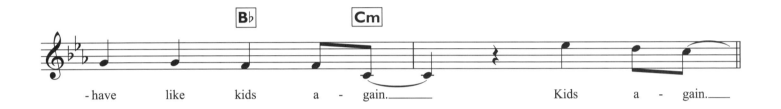

- have like kids a - gain._____ Kids a - gain._____

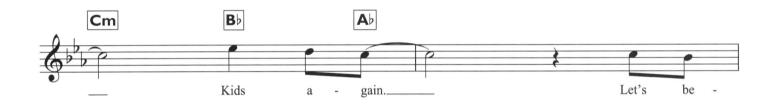

___ Kids a - gain._____ Let's be -

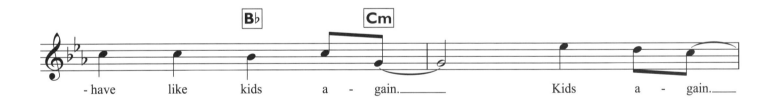

- have like kids a - gain._____ Kids a - gain.____

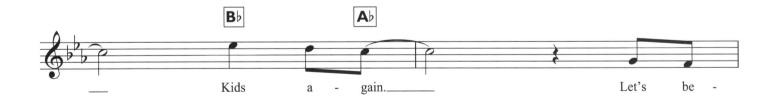

___ Kids a - gain._____ Let's be -

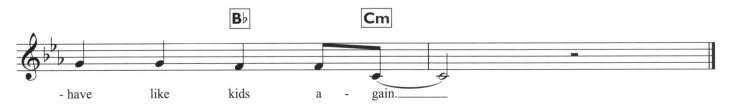

- have like kids a - gain._____

21

LET GO FOR TONIGHT

Words & Music by Thomas Hull & Louisa Allen

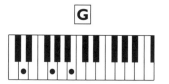
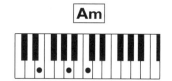
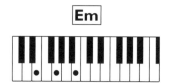
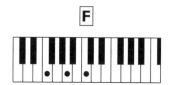

Voice: **Piano**

Rhythm: **Hard Rock**

Tempo: ♩ = 140

Fell from the sky.___ We fell from the sky___ and start-ed walk-

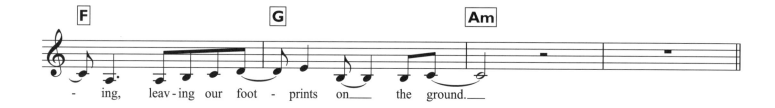

- ing, leav-ing our foot - prints on___ the ground.___

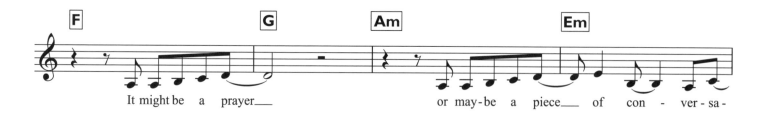

It might be a prayer___ or may-be a piece___ of con - ver-sa-

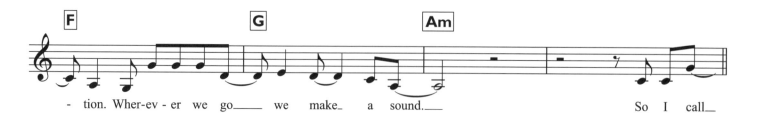

- tion. Wher-ev - er we go___ we make___ a sound.___ So I call___

___ your name,___ the on - ly thing I know___ is I need___ you here___ or you'll be

22

gone for - ev - er. All that I know, all that I know___ is we're here___

___ to - night._____ Turn off the lights.___ Let go for to - night___

___ ba - by. Let love in your life___ and be___ strong.___

Let go for to - night___ ba - by. Who needs sleep___ to - night.___

_____ I need to let go, let it go.___

Let go, let it go._____ Turn off the lights.___ Let love in your life___

___ ba - by. Who needs sleep___ to - night._____

LET IT GO

Words & Music by Robert Lopez & Kristen Anderson-Lopez

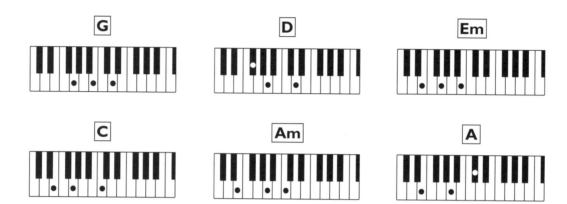

Voice: **Flute**

Rhythm: **16 Rock**

Tempo: ♩ = **70**

Let it go.___ Let it go.___ Can't hold it back an - y - more.___ Let it go.___

___ Let it go.___ Turn my back and slam__ the door. The

snow glows white on the moun-tain to - night.__ Not a foot-print to be___ seen. A

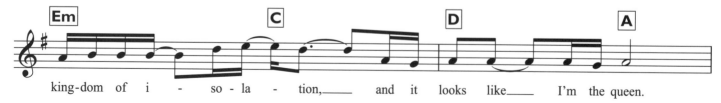

king-dom of i - so - la - tion,___ and it looks like___ I'm the queen.

The wind_ is howl - ing like_ this swirl - ing storm in - side._

Could-n't keep it in,_ heav - en knows I_ tried.

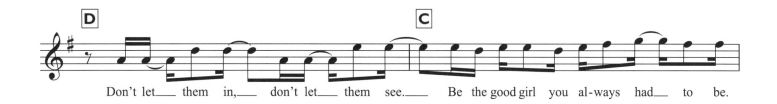

Don't let_ them in,_ don't let_ them see._ Be the good girl you al-ways had_ to be.

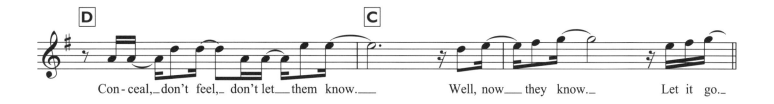

Con - ceal,_ don't feel,_ don't let_ them know._ Well, now_ they know._ Let it go._

_ Let it go._ Can't hold it back an - y - more._ Let it go._ Let it go._ Turn my

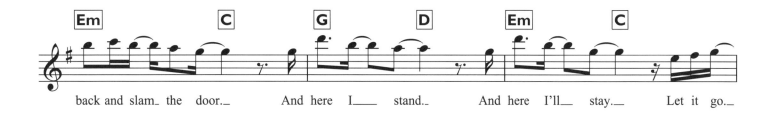

back and slam_ the door._ And here I_ stand._ And here I'll_ stay._ Let it go._

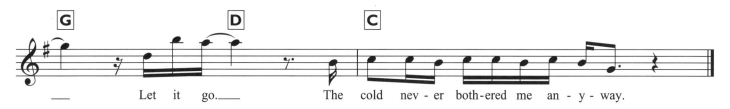

_ Let it go._ The cold nev - er both-ered me an - y - way.

LET ME GO

Words & Music by Gary Barlow

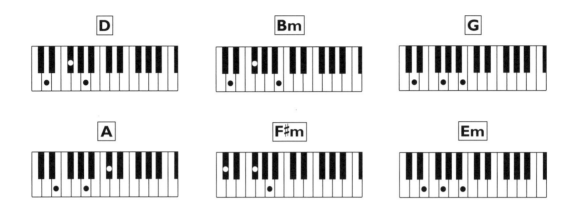

Voice: **Acoustic Guitar**

Rhythm: **Folk Rock**

Tempo: ♩ = 130

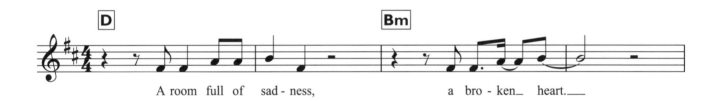

A room full of sad - ness, a bro - ken_ heart.__

And on - ly__ me__ to blame_ for ev - 'ry__ sin - gle part.__

No sci - ence or re - li - gion could make this_ whole.__

To be loved, but_ nev - er love._ To have, but_ nev - er hold. It's a

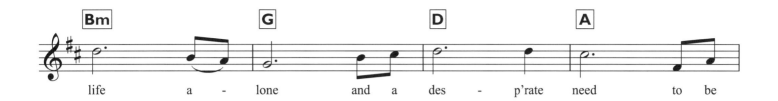

life a - lone and a des - p'rate need to be

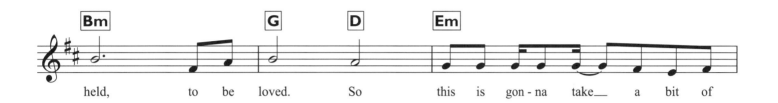

held, to be loved. So this is gon - na take__ a bit of

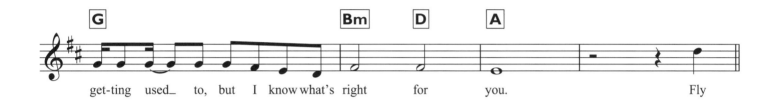

get-ting used__ to, but I know what's right for you. Fly

high__ and let me go. That

sky__ will save your soul. When you pass__

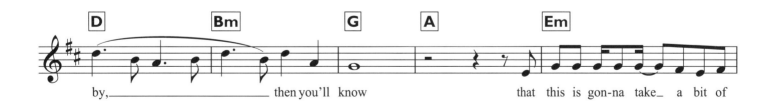

by,__ then you'll know that this is gon - na take__ a bit of

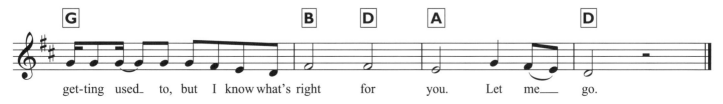

get-ting used__ to, but I know what's right for you. Let me__ go.

27

LITTLE ME

Words & Music by Thomas Barnes, Peter Kelleher, Benjamin Kohn, Iain James, Jessica Nelson, Jade Thirlwall, Perrie Edwards & Leigh-Anne Pinnock

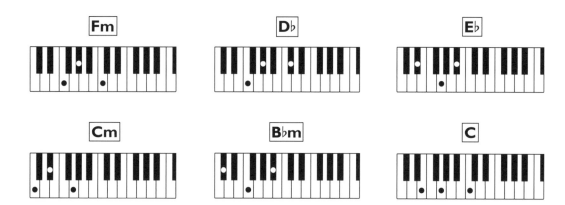

Voice: **Acoustic Guitar**

Rhythm: **R 'n' B**

Tempo: ♩ = 82

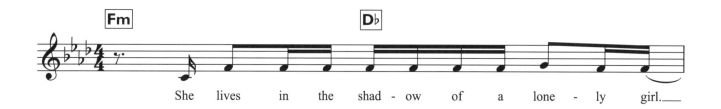

She lives in the shad - ow of a lone - ly girl.

Voice so qui - et you don't hear a word.

Al - ways talk - ing but she can't be heard.

You can see it there if you catch her eye.

Eb — Cm
— I know she's brave but she's trapped in - side.—

Db — Bbm
— Scared to talk,— but she don't know

C
why.— Wish I knew back

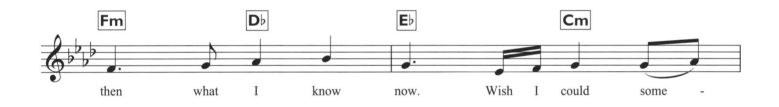

Fm — Db — Eb — Cm
then what I know now. Wish I could some -

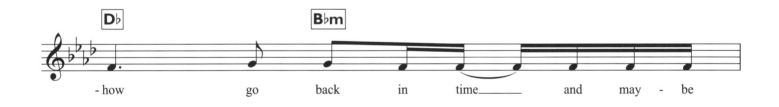

Db — Bbm
- how go back in time— and may - be

C
lis - ten to my own ad - vice.— I'd tell her to speak—

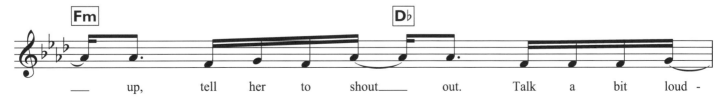

Fm — Db
— up, tell her to shout— out. Talk a bit loud -

29

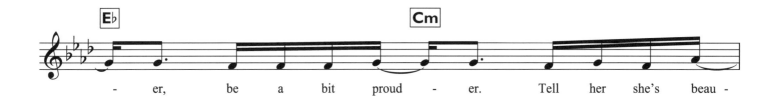

-er, be a bit proud - er. Tell her she's beau -

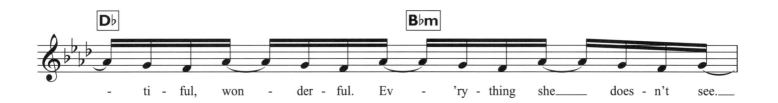

- ti - ful, won - der - ful. Ev - 'ry - thing she____ does - n't see.____

____ You got - ta speak____

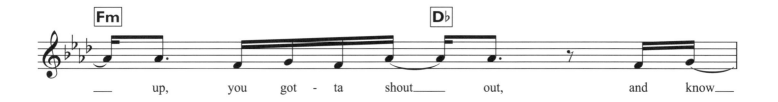

____ up, you got - ta shout____ out, and know____

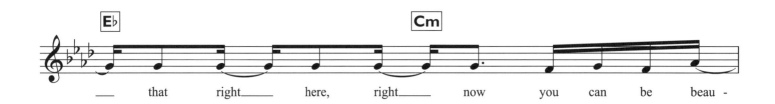

____ that right____ here, right____ now you can be beau -

- ti - ful, won - der - ful. An - y - thing you____ wan - na be.____

____ Lit - tle____ me.____

THINGS WE LOST IN THE FIRE

Words & Music by Daniel Campbell Smith

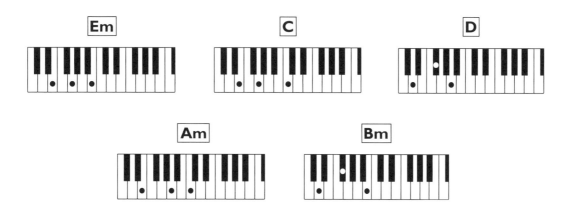

Voice: **Piano**

Rhythm: **Rock 2**

Tempo: ♩ = 132

Things we lost to the flames.

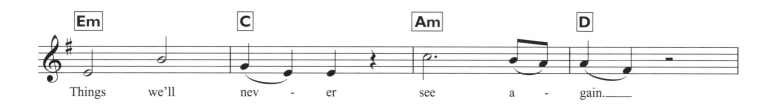

Things we'll nev - er see a - gain.

All that we have a - massed

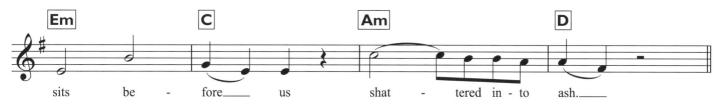

sits be - fore us shat - tered in - to ash.

These are the things, the things we lost,___ the things we lost___ in the

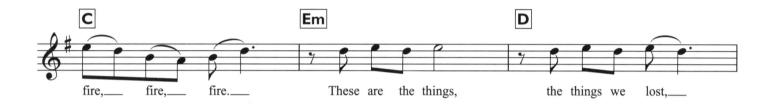

fire,___ fire,___ fire.___ These are the things, the things we lost,___

the things we lost___ in the fire,___ fire,___ fire.___

We sat___ and made___ a list___ of all the things__ that we had,_

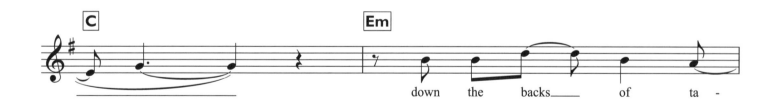

___ down the backs___ of ta -

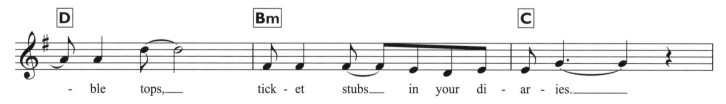

- ble tops,___ tick - et stubs___ in your di - ar - ies.___

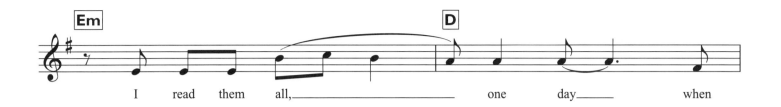

I read them all, one day when

lone - li - ness came and you were a - way. Oh, they told me

noth - ing new but I love to read the words you use.

These are the things, the things we lost,

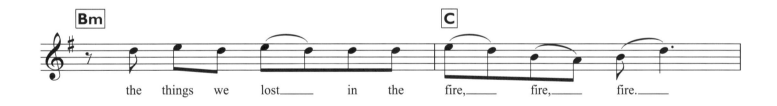

the things we lost in the fire, fire, fire.

These are the things, the things we lost,

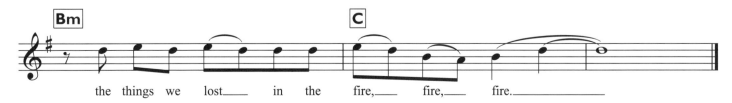

the things we lost in the fire, fire, fire.

MAGIC

Words & Music by Guy Berryman, Jonathan Buckland, William Champion & Christopher Martin

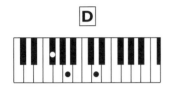
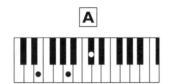
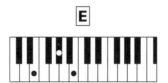
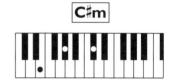

Voice: **Rock Organ**

Rhythm: **Rumba**

Tempo: ♩ = 120

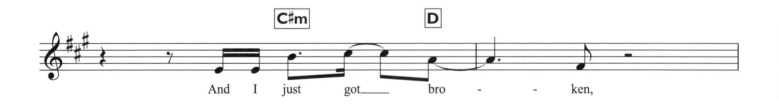

Still I call it__ ma - - gic

when I'm next to__ you.   And I

don't and I don't and I don't and I don't,_   no, I don't, it's true.   I

don't, no, I don't, no, I don't, no, I don't_   want an - y - bod - y else but   you.   I

don't, no, I don't, no, I don't, no, I don't,_   no, I don't, it's true.   I

don't, no, I don't, no, I don't, no, I don't_   want an - y - bod - y else but   you.

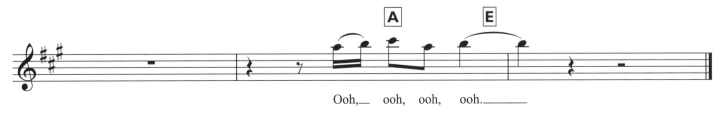

Ooh,__ ooh, ooh, ooh._____

RATHER BE

Words & Music by James Napier, Grace Chatto & Jack Patterson
© Copyright 2014 Salli Isaak Songs Limited.
Universal Music Publishing Limited/EMI Music Publishing Limited/Sony/ATV Music Publishing Limited.
All Rights Reserved. International Copyright Secured.

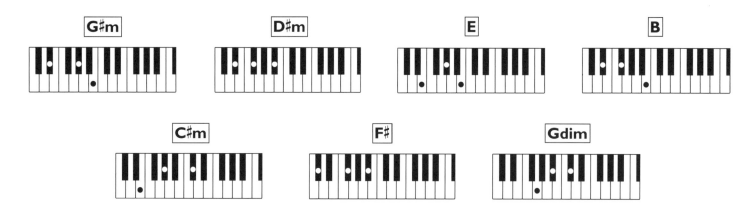

Voice: **Violin**

Rhythm: **Dance Pop**

Tempo: ♩ = 120

We're a thou-sand miles from com - fort. We have trav-elled land and sea.___ But as

long as you are with___ me, there's no place___ I'd ra - ther be.___

I would wait for-ev - er, ex-ult-ed in the scene.___ As

long as I am with___ you, my heart___ con-tin-ues___ to beat.

With ev-'ry step we take, Ky-o-to to the Bay. Stroll-ing__ so ca-sual-ly.__

We're diff-'rent and the same, get you an-oth-er name. Switch up__ the bat-ter-ies.__

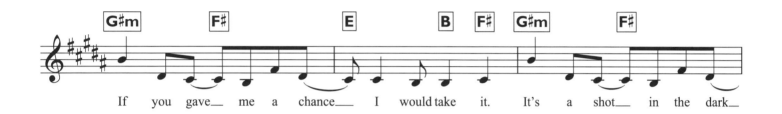

If you gave__ me a chance__ I would take it. It's a shot__ in the dark__

__ but I'll make it. Know with all__ of your heart__ you can't__ shame me.

When I__ am with you__ there's no place__ I'd rath-er__ be.__ N, n, no, no,__ no.

No place I'd ra-ther be. N, n, no, no,__ no. No place I'd ra-ther be.

N, n, no, no,__ no. No place I'd ra-ther be.

ROAR

**Words & Music by Katy Perry, Lukasz Gottwald, Bonnie McKee, Martin Max
& Henry Russell Walter**

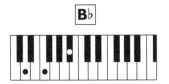 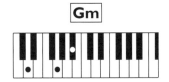  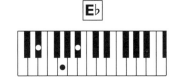

Voice: **Alto Saxophone**

Rhythm: **Rock I**

Tempo: ♩ = 88

hear my voice, you hear that sound.__ Like thun - der gon - na shake the ground. You

held me down but I got up. Get read - y 'cause I've had e - nough. I

see it all. I see it now. I got the eye of the ti - ger, a fight - er danc-

-ing through the fire.___'Cause I____ am a cham - pion and you're gon - na hear__ me__ roar.__

____ Loud - er, lou - der than the li - on. 'Cause I____ am a cham - pion and

you're gon - na hear__ me__ roar.____ Oh, oh, oh, oh, oh.____ Oh,__ oh, oh, oh, oh, oh.____

Oh,__ oh, oh, oh, oh, oh.____ You're gon - na hear__ me roar.____

SHE LOOKS SO PERFECT

Words & Music by Michael Clifford, Ashton Irwin & Jacob Sinclair

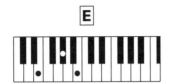
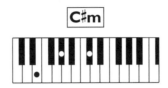
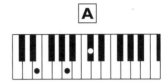

Voice: **Electric Guitar**

Rhythm: **Hard Rock**

Tempo: ♩ = 80

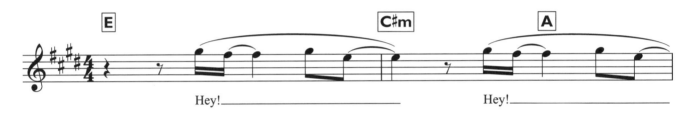

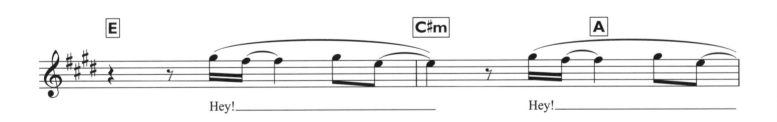

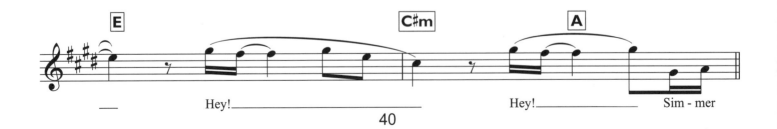

down.___ Sim-mer down.___ They say we're too young now to a-mount to an - y - thing else.___

____ But look a - round.___ We worked too damn hard for this____ just to give it up now.___

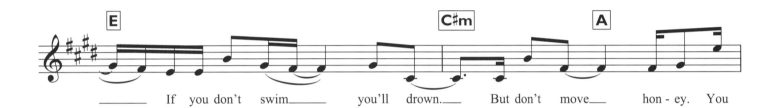

____ If you don't swim____ you'll drown.___ But don't move____ hon - ey. You

look so per - fect stand - ing there___ in my A - mer - i - can Ap-par - el un - der-wear.___ And

I know___ now,____ that I'm so____ down.___ Your

lip - stick stain___ is a work of art.___ I got your name tat - tooed in an ar - row heart.___ And

I know___ now,____ that I'm so____ down.___ (Hey, hey!)

SOMEWHERE ONLY WE KNOW

Words & Music by Richard Hughes, Tim Rice-Oxley & Tom Chaplin

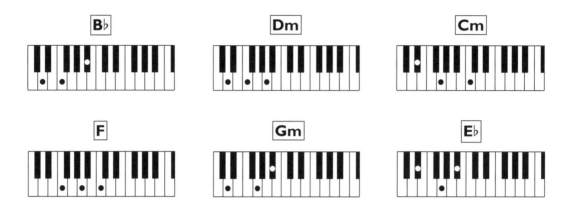

Voice: **Piano & Strings**

Rhythm: **Slow Rock**

Tempo: ♩ = 84

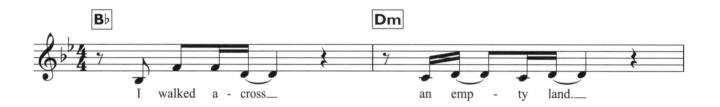

I walked a-cross___ an emp-ty land.___

I knew the path - way like the back of my hand.___

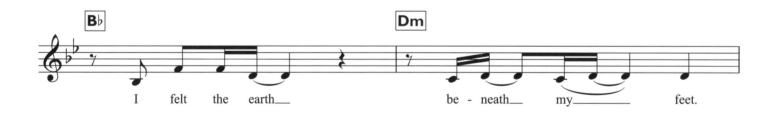

I felt the earth___ be-neath___ my___ feet.

Sat by the riv - er and it made me com - plete.___

Oh, sim - ple thing, where have you gone?

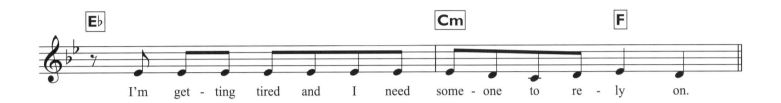

I'm get - ting tired and I need some - one to re - ly on.

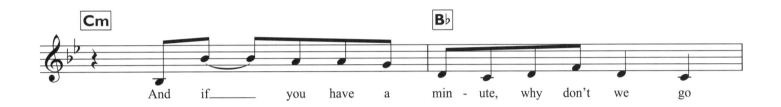

And if you have a min - ute, why don't we go

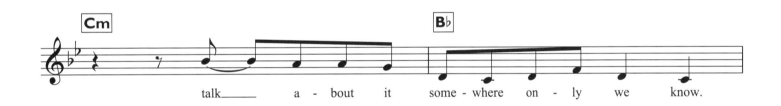

talk a - bout it some - where on - ly we know.

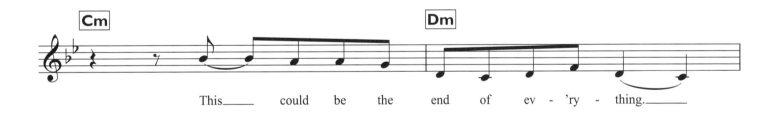

This could be the end of ev - 'ry - thing.

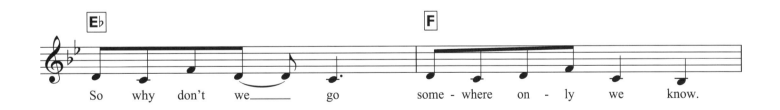

So why don't we go some - where on - ly we know.

Some - where on - ly we know.

STORY OF MY LIFE

Words & Music by John Ryan, Jamie Scott, Julian Bunetta, Harry Styles,
Niall Horan, Liam Payne, Louis Tomlinson & Zayn Malik

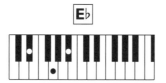
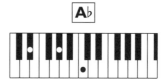
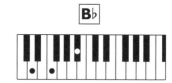

Voice: **Acoustic Guitar**

Rhythm: **Folk Rock**

Tempo: ♩ = 120

Writ-ten in___ these walls are the sto-ries that I can't ex - plain. I

leave my___ heart o - pen___ but it stays right___ here emp - ty___ for days.

She told me in the morn-ing she don't feel the same a - bout us in her

bones. It seems to me___ that when I die___ these

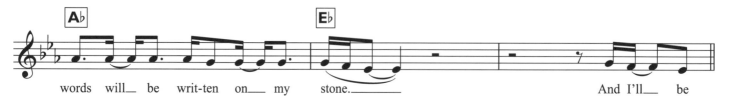

words will___ be writ-ten on___ my stone.___ And I'll___ be

gone, gone to-night.___ The ground be-neath___ my feet is o - pen wide.___ The way that I___ been

hold - in' on___ too tight___ with noth-ing in___ be - tween. The

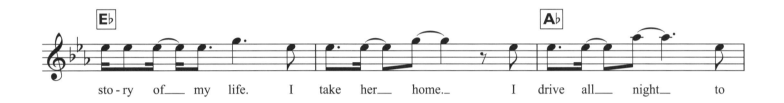

sto - ry of___ my life. I take her___ home.___ I drive all___ night___ to

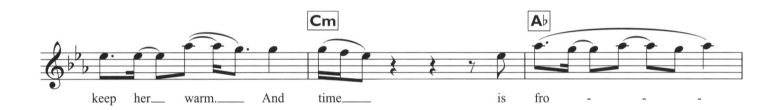

keep her___ warm.___ And time___ is fro - - -

- zen.___ The sto - ry of___ my life. I

give her___ hope.___ I spend her___ love___ un - til she's___ broke___ in -

- side.___ The sto - ry of___ my life.___

YOUNG BLOOD

Words & Music by Sophie Ellis Bextor & Ed Harcourt

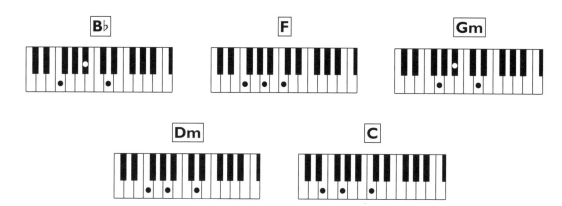

Voice: **Piano**

Rhythm: **Slow Rock**

Tempo: ♩ = 60

The days   are ghost   that pass right through us.   In my

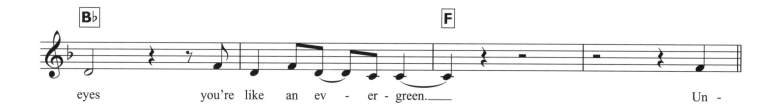

eyes   you're like an ev - er - green.___   Un -

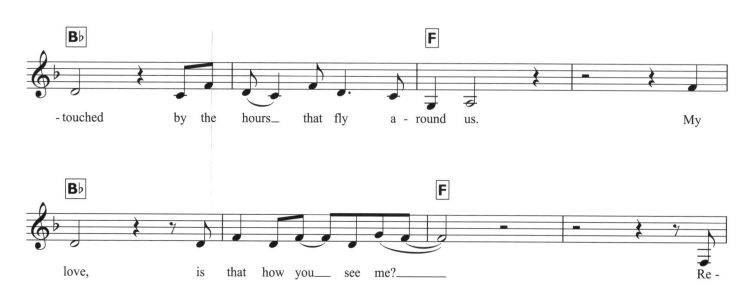

-touched   by the hours___ that fly   a - round   us.   My

love,   is that how you___ see me?___   Re -

-mem-ber when,___ re-mem-ber when we were the dia-monds in___ the coal.___

Lov-ers know there's no age up-on___ your soul.___ It's all o-kay, you give me

young___ blood.___ It's cours-ing through my veins, it's real___ love.___

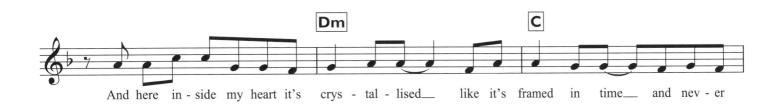

And here in-side my heart it's crys-tal-lised___ like it's framed in time___ and nev-er

taint-ed.___ Yeah, it's al-right, you give me young___ blood.___

Be-fore the world I may be old e-nough.___ There'll be a day to take the

best of us.___ But till___ then___ we have young___ blood.___

47

Bringing you the words and the music

All the latest music in print... rock & pop plus jazz, blues, country, classical and the best in West End show scores.

- Books to match your favourite CDs.

- Book-and-CD titles with high quality backing tracks for you to play along to. Now you can play guitar or piano with your favourite artist... or simply sing along!

- Audition songbooks with CD backing tracks for both male and female singers for all those with stars in their eyes.

- Can't read music? No problem, you can still play all the hits with our wide range of chord songbooks.

- Check out our range of instrumental tutorial titles, taking you from novice to expert in no time at all!

- Musical show scores include *The Phantom Of The Opera*, *Les Misérables*, *Mamma Mia* and many more hit productions.

- DVD master classes featuring the techniques of top artists.